DINOSAURS
Giants of the Past

DINOSAURS
Giants of the Past

By Eileen Daly
Illustrated by Rod Ruth

MERRIGOLD PRESS • NEW YORK

Library of Congress Catalog Card Number: 74-4404 ISBN: 0-307-10939-9 MCMXCII

Millions of years ago, Earth was very different from the way it is now. It was warm everywhere. There were many volcanos and earthquakes. And there were no people at all; dinosaurs ruled the world. Right where you live, there may have been a jungle or a swamp filled with strange plants . . . and dinosaurs.

Dinosaurs liked to live near water, where there were plants for food and a place to wade and keep cool. At that time, there was plenty of water; more than half of our present United States was covered with deep lakes.

All baby dinosaurs came from eggs. A mother dinosaur laid her eggs in a nest of leaves or sand. From those eggs came some of the biggest and strangest animals ever to walk the Earth. Most dinosaurs did not live together in families. When the baby dinosaurs hatched from their eggs, they crawled away from the nest and never returned.

Without a mother or father taking care of it, a baby dinosaur must have had a hard life. As soon as it hatched from its egg, a dinosaur baby had to find its own food and try to keep out of the way of other, bigger dinosaurs that might try to eat it.

Di-PLOD-o-cus

Diplodocus was the longest land animal that ever lived. It was nearly one hundred feet long from its nose to the tip of its tail—as long as eight or nine cars in a row. Diplodocus had a small mouth and weak, peglike teeth. It had to spend most of its time eating hundreds of pounds of plants every day to nourish its huge body.

Diplodocus could stand in one place—on legs as big around as tree trunks—stretch out its long neck, and nibble plants thirty feet away from where it stood!

The biggest land animal ever was Brachiosaurus. It was as heavy as a thousand men and looked mean and fearsome. But Brachiosaurus was clumsy and slow and could easily be caught by its enemies. It did have a good way to protect itself without having to fight: When an enemy came, Brachiosaurus could walk into a deep lake almost to the top of its head. There, it could breathe through nose openings in a little dome at the very top of its head and stay under the water till the enemy went away.

When it was on land, Brachiosaurus probably looked like a big hill. Its great pillar-like front legs were longer than its hind legs, and its head was forty feet from the ground!

Brachiosaurus spent its time eating and sleeping; it did very little thinking. Though its body weighed as much as eighty-five tons, this dinosaur heavyweight had a brain only the size of an apple.

Brach-i-o-SAU-rus

Ty-ran-no-SAU-rus Rex

Some dinosaurs were very fierce. Two-legged Tyrannosaurus Rex was the fiercest of them all. It was the largest meat-eating animal ever to live on Earth. Its giant head was mostly mouth, and in that mouth were rows of teeth like six-inch knives. Tyrannosaurus could open its huge mouth four feet wide and could easily swallow, in one gulp, most animals that live today! Its strange, short arms were useless, but its great muscular legs had strong, sharp claws. Nothing that lived was safe from the gigantic Tyrannosaurus Rex.

The head of Pachycephalosaurus was covered by a cap of solid bone nine inches thick. But the rest of this medium-sized dinosaur's body was unprotected, and it often made a tempting meal for a giant meat eater.

Some dinosaurs looked frightful but were really peaceful and harmless.

Stegosaurus grew rows of bony armor along its back and four bony spikes on its tail to help keep it safe from its enemies. Stegosaurus was a slow mover and ate only plants. If attacked, it would swing its heavy, spiked tail from side to side trying to hit the enemy. Stegosaurus was bigger than an elephant, but its head was very small—and there was not much room in it for a brain.

Styracosaurus always had to face an enemy if attacked, because it grew its armor only on its head. It wore a collar of long, sharp spikes, and a large horn grew on its snout. Its strong, beaklike mouth was also sharp, though it was used only to eat plants.

Styracosaurus was a little larger than a rhinoceros. It, too, was clumsy and slow and had a very small brain.

Tri-CER-a-tops

Triceratops was also well equipped to defend itself from the front if attacked. It had two long, strong horns above its eyes and a shorter horn over its parrot-like mouth. Behind the horns rose a great bony shield which helped to protect the rest of its body from enemies.

Today, scientists think that Triceratops was one of the few dinosaurs that roamed the plains in large herds.

Not all dinosaurs were giants. Compsognathus was one of the smaller well-known dinosaurs. It was about the size of a rooster; its head was about three and a half inches long.

Compsognathus could run very fast on its hind legs to catch its food and escape from enemies. It probably ate insects and other small reptiles.

Oviraptor was also a small dinosaur, only about three feet long. It had no teeth, so it ate soft foods like fruits and berries and insects. Often, Oviraptor would crack open the eggs of other dinosaurs and suck them dry. Its name means "egg robber."

Like Compsognathus, Oviraptor's only defense against enemies was its speed.

Though there were many dinosaurs of all types on Earth millions of years ago, no man ever saw a live dinosaur. Dinosaurs disappeared before there were people on Earth.

How do we know that dinosaurs ever lived and what they looked like? We can tell by the bones they left behind. Men have found the bones of dinosaurs, now called fossils, and put them together. Today, giant fossil dinosaurs stand in museums.

It's exciting to learn about the dinosaurs by studying their bones and the footprints that they left behind.

Can you imagine a footprint big enough to play in?